Rope Burn

Jan Siebold

SCHOLASTIC INC.
New York Toronto London Auckland Sydney
Mexico City New Delhi Hong Kong Buenos Aires

ISBN 0-439-32237-5

12 11 10 9 8 7 6 5 4 3 2 1   1 2 3 4 5 6/0

Printed in the U.S.A.   40

First Scholastic printing, November 2001

Design and dingbats by Scott Piehl.

Contents

The Assignment. . . 5

Proverb One. . . 12
ONE GOOD TURN DESERVES ANOTHER
or How I Retrieved Something Valuable from
a Deserted House

Proverb Two. . . 24
HE WHO HESITATES IS LOST
or How I Met James

Proverb Three. . . 39
WHEN IN ROME, DO AS THE ROMANS DO
or My Secret Weekend Life

Proverb Four. . . 45
IF AT FIRST YOU DON'T SUCCEED, TRY, TRY AGAIN
or How My Writing Has Improved

Proverb Five. . . 48
ABSENCE MAKES THE HEART GROW FONDER
or The First Time I Saw a Dead Body

298
+24
$3.22

Proverb Six. . . 55
A PENNY SAVED IS A PENNY EARNED
or How I Bought My Deluxe Colored Pencil Set

Proverb Seven. . . 63
TOO MANY COOKS SPOIL THE BROTH
or How Mom and I Created
Volcanic Salsa

Proverb Eight. . . 67
HASTE MAKES WASTE
or How I Slipped in Crawford Creek

Proverb Nine. . . 77
THE PEN IS MIGHTIER THAN THE SWORD
or How My Voice Was Heard

The Assignment

I hate writing.

At least, I hate the kind of writing that most teachers expect. Where do they come up with those ideas for assignments, anyway?

I swear, all teachers must have been required to take a college course called "Student Torture 101." Mr. Best, my English teacher, must have gotten an "A."

I started out liking him this year. He actually has a sense of humor sometimes. I just wish I could figure out what he wants from me.

Which brings me to Mr. Best's latest brainstorm. We've been learning about proverbs in English class. (In case you don't know what a proverb is, don't worry. We had to memorize the definition. It's "a brief popular saying based on common sense or experience which illustrates a point." Example: "One bad apple doesn't spoil the whole bunch.")

Mr. Best had the brilliant idea that we should write a composition about a proverb that illustrates something that has happened in our lives. He gave us a whole list of proverbs to choose from.

My friend James thinks that the assignment is one of our easier ones. He already has his idea. He's going to use the proverb "You can't teach an old dog new tricks." His composition is going to be about his parents' attempts to quit smoking.

James told me that the longest they've ever gone without smoking is three months. He has tried to convince them to quit. He even left his health textbook opened to the chapter called "The Effects of Tobacco Smoke," but it didn't seem to help.

I've been at James's house during some of those nonsmoking periods. You could almost cut the tension with a knife. The eating has usually been good during those times, though. When Mr. and Mrs. Buchanan aren't smoking, they make up for it by eating a lot.

Once when I was there, they actually had a huge shouting match over who finished the last piece of chocolate layer cake. They seemed pretty embarrassed about it later on. James said that they each lit up a cigarette as soon as I left.

Don't get me wrong--Mr. and Mrs. Buchanan are nice people. James really wishes that they would stop smoking, but he has come to realize that they probably won't change. You can't teach an old dog new tricks.

James looks at it this way: old dogs are comfortable to be around.

It's not that I can't think of something to write about. I've got lots of ideas floating around in my brain. In fact, I've enjoyed writing stories and comic books since I was little. My fifth-grade teacher even told me that I could be a writer someday. I wish she would tell that to Mr. Best.

So far this fall, every paper that I've written for him has been a struggle. Each week since September, he has assigned a composition of our choice. I would try to write a really good one that included lots of different points of view. But he never gave me anything higher than a "C." Mr. Best's comments were always something like "I want to know what YOU think, Richard," or "Your thoughts are scattered. What is your point?"

Looking back, I guess I did try to cram a lot into those papers. There is a lot that I've wanted to say lately.

Last time, I tried an experiment. I

decided to open an encyclopedia to any page and point to a topic. I figured that I couldn't go wrong with just plain facts. The subject I happened to pick was "carbon." Don't worry. I'm not stupid enough to copy an encyclopedia article word-for-word. Mr. Best would probably turn me over to the FBI for that. I read the article and picked out the most interesting facts. Believe me when I tell you that carbon is not that interesting. Then I rewrote the information in my own words and handed it in.

This time, I got a "B+," along with a note to "see me after class."

"Richard," Mr. Best began, "you obviously put forth some effort on this latest assignment. You organized your ideas into a nice, cohesive framework."

Why don't English teachers just speak plain English, I wonder?

Mr. Best continued, "However, the subject is a bit unusual. I'm interested in knowing how you came up with it."

I paused to think. Mr. Best would probably not appreciate hearing about my game of encyclopedia roulette.

"Well...uh...I was staring at my pencil point, trying to think of a topic, and that's when I came up with the idea of carbon."

"I see. How very interesting," Mr. Best said. He picked up the list of proverbs from a pile on his desk. "Have you decided which proverb to choose for the next assignment?"

"Actually, a lot of them fit my life," I answered. "I might try writing about some of them and see which turns out the best."

Mr. Best looked at me.

"Richard," he said. "You need to find your writing voice."

I must have looked confused, because he went on to explain.

"Somehow I think that you're trying to write what I want to read, not what you want to write. The real you doesn't come through in your compositions. It's okay to express your feelings or opinions when you write. Just try to be yourself, Richard. Why don't you think about it for this assignment."

●

So I have been thinking about it. I keep listening and listening, Mr. Best, but I don't hear a voice.

Proverb One

ONE GOOD TURN DESERVES ANOTHER
or How I Retrieved Something
Valuable from a Deserted House

For the first eleven years of my life, I lived in a huge old house on the other side of town. The neighborhood was very quiet because a lot of the people who lived there were pretty old. Most of the houses were at least three stories high. Ours was charcoal gray with white shutters. It had a wide porch with a roof that was supported by big white columns. That porch was a great place to play.

Harry and Vi Marshall lived on one side of us. They were a retired couple whose kids had all grown up and moved away. Vi was really nice. Harry was grumpy most of the time. He was always sucking on a piece of hard candy that smelled like licorice. It's funny--Vi insisted that I call them by their first names, but I could never bring myself to call Harry anything but "Mr. Marshall." I don't think he ever forgave me for the time I rode my bike on his new driveway before the concrete had hardened. You can still see the tracks.

The Marshalls had a cottage on Spruce Lake, so they weren't around much in the summertime. Whenever they were at the lake, we would take in their mail and newspaper and water their plants.

When I got to be old enough, my mom would give me the key to the Marshalls' house and let me take care of things. I had a regular ritual that I performed each time. First, I would unlock the front door and walk into the hallway. Then I would say very loudly, "I guess I'll bring in the mail and paper now."

This was to give any possible robbers a chance to run out the back door. That may sound silly, but the old house could be very spooky when nobody was there. Vi had always drawn the drapes before leaving, so the house was shadowy and dark.

Once, when I was there alone, the grandfather clock in the hallway decided to chime loudly just as I was walking past it. I almost had a heart attack.

Next, I would get the mail and paper and carry it all into the kitchen. I even sorted the letters, magazines, and newspapers into three neat piles on the kitchen table.

Once a week, I would get Vi's small green watering can from underneath the sink and water all of the plants in the kitchen and dining room. Vi always insisted that the plants looked healthier after she and Harry had been away. She said that I must have a magic touch.

Last of all, I would lock the front door, check about three times to make sure it was really locked, and go home.

One day, I was almost finished with my ritual. I was just about to leave when I heard a hissing and sputtering noise coming from the back bedroom. I froze.

I stood there for about five minutes, trying to figure out what the noise could be. It didn't sound like any human or animal I'd heard. Finally, I got up enough nerve to tiptoe to the bedroom doorway and peek inside.

What I saw was Vi's steam iron sitting upright on the ironing board, making those noises. I walked over and saw that the iron had been left on. I poked at the lever to push it over to the "off" position. It was very hot to touch. Then I unplugged the iron and left.

When I got home, I told my mom about the iron. She mentioned it to Vi and Harry when they got home. Harry didn't say much, but you would have thought I deserved a medal the way Vi carried on. She hugged me and said that I had probably saved their house from burning down. She even tried to give me some money, but Mom said I was just being a good neighbor, and wouldn't let me take it.

●

The iron incident happened during our last summer in that house. The next spring, my mom and dad split up, and we sold the house. My mom and I moved to a smaller house across town, and my dad took an apartment a few blocks from his business.

Mom and Dad kept trying to reassure me that things weren't going to change that much. They said that I'd still be spending as much time with each of them. How could they think that the change to a new house, a new neighborhood, a new school, and a whole new way of life wasn't that drastic? Even ONE of those things would have been hard for a kid to handle.

I must admit that the new house isn't so bad. It has a great front porch. My bedroom takes up practically the whole upstairs. It has a big open middle area,

with ceilings that slope down on each
side. Mom let me put baseball posters on
the slanted ceilings. They'd never let
me tack up posters in the old house.

About a month after Mom and I had
moved into the new house, I was upstairs
unpacking some boxes. Back then, I re-
treated to my room when Mom was talking
on the phone to one of her friends. She
was usually complaining about Dad, and I
didn't really want to hear it.

Anyway, I was unpacking my desk stuff
when I came across my book bank. It
looked just like an old leather-bound
book. It had a little gold key that you
put into a keyhole on the "page" side of
the bank. When you lifted the cover,
there was an empty metal-lined space for
storing valuables.

My dad had given it to me a few years
before. He had gotten it when he opened
up his first savings account as a little boy. The gold letters on the cover
were wearing away, but they still looked

beautiful against the red leather cover.

The bank held a new penny from the year I was born, a few of my all-time favorite baseball cards, and some stories and comics that I had written.

As I took my book bank out of the cardboard box, it occurred to me that I had left the key in its secret hiding place back at the old house. I kept my key on a ledge just inside my closet door.

I realized that if I ever wanted to see those things again, I'd either have to pry open the bank or get my key back. I hated the thought of ruining something special that my dad had given to me. I had to have that key.

Shortly after we moved, Mom discovered that she had forgotten to take a brass key holder off the kitchen wall of our old house. She figured that it legally belonged to the new owners now.

Well, they couldn't have MY key, I decided. I would take the crosstown bus back to my old neighborhood and ask the new owners for my key. I would tell them about my parents' split and say that the key was special because my dad had given it to me. How could they refuse?

I was used to taking the bus around town. Ever since Mom went back to work at her old office, I would take the bus downtown to meet Dad for lunch, or go to my favorite baseball card store.

By two o'clock the next day, I was standing in front of my old house. The house looked pretty much the same, except the new owners had nailed a wooden "Welcome" sign next to the front door. I hoped that they really meant it. The sign had a gold pineapple painted on it. I wondered what pineapples had to do with welcoming people.

I had been practicing what to say all the way there on the bus, so before I lost my nerve, I went up the steps and rang the doorbell.

No one answered. I couldn't believe it. I'd come all that way, and no one was home. I walked around to the backyard to make sure nobody was there. There were no cars in the garage or driveway, and the backyard was empty.

I was standing in the driveway trying to decide what to do, when suddenly a gruff voice startled me.

"Richard? Is that you?"

I whirled around. A cloud of licorice breath hit me in the face. "Oh, hi, Mr. Marshall," I stammered.

Harry stared at me. "What are you doing here?" he asked.

"Uh, I just stopped by to see the old place. Is Vi here?" Vi would understand my predicament and be able to help me, I was sure.

"No. She's at the hairdresser."

Harry continued to stare at me. He seemed smaller and thinner than I remembered, like he'd shrunk since we moved away. "Is something wrong?" he asked.

"No. Well, not exactly," I replied. We stood there, just looking at each other for a minute. Oh well, I thought, what do I have to lose?

"You see, I left something important inside the house, and I came to get it," I explained. I went on to tell Harry about the key.

He didn't laugh or snort like I thought he might. "I see," he said. "Well, actually they won't be back until next week. They're on vacation. They left us their key so that we can get their mail and feed their cat."

I looked down at the driveway and nudged a stone with the toe of my sneaker.

Harry paused and then went on slowly, "It wouldn't be right to let someone else into their house."

I must have looked pitiful, because Harry seemed to be really thinking over the situation. Finally he announced, "Well, I don't see the harm in letting you in for just a minute to get your key. After all, you're not exactly a stranger to the house."

A few minutes later, Harry was unlocking the front door. "I'll wait here," he said. Then he added, "And don't touch anything, Richard."

I figured he said that last part to keep up his image of a grump.

I hurried through the house. It seemed really strange to see someone else's furniture in our old house. My mom and dad had worked very hard to refinish the wooden bannister, and the new owners had painted it white. Pictures of strangers lined the stairway. In one picture, a man, woman, and little girl sat in the crook of a large tree, smiling like the perfect little family that they probably were.

In my room, a double bed with a pink ruffled cover stood where my twin bed had stood. My clutter of books, baseball cards, games, and clothes had been replaced by someone else's stuffed animals, dolls, and toys.

I was suddenly angrier than I had ever been before. I just wanted to kick or hit something. I was so mad, I was shaking. Why should I have to act like a stranger in my own bedroom? Luckily, just then I heard Harry at the bottom of the stairs.

"Richard?" he called.

"Be right there," I answered. I went to the closet and felt up along the ledge. My key was still there. I put it in my pocket and went downstairs without even looking at anything else. I just wanted to get out of there.

Harry locked the front door, and we went down the steps.

"Goodbye, Harry," I said. "Thanks for letting me in. Say hi to Vi for me." I turned to leave.

Harry cleared his throat. "You know, Richard, I'll always remember the time you found that iron turned on. I just thought I'd return the favor today."

Harry held out his hand and I shook it. It felt cold and feeble.

I started to walk back to the bus stop. A few houses away, I turned around. Harry was still standing there watching me. We both waved, and I went home.

Proverb Two

HE WHO HESITATES IS LOST
or How I Met James

One of the worst things that can happen to a kid is having to move to a new school. You don't know where you're going, you don't know any of the teachers, and you don't have any friends. It's an open invitation for humiliation.

I figured that the best way to survive was to blend in like a chameleon. If you're new, the minute you stand out or call attention to yourself, you're dead. That first week of school, I was careful to wear the standard uniform of most kids my age: jeans, a T-shirt, and sneakers. I have shaggy blond hair and brown eyes. I guess I'm pretty average-looking.

The first few days went by without any major problems. The routine was pretty much the same as in my old school. The teachers gave their beginning-of-the-year speeches about homework and expectations and stuff, and handed out books. The other kids were still getting used to the shock of being back in school, so they didn't even seem to notice me.

Things were going along well until Friday. That was the day I had my first gym class. Right away, the gym teacher, Mr. Reynolds, announced that we would be starting the year with a basic physical education test. He said that he wanted to see where we all stood. The test was to be made up of four stations: sit-ups, push-ups, laps, and rope-climbing.

When I heard him say "rope-climbing," I broke into a cold sweat. I had never been able to climb a rope at my old school. But at least there, it wasn't required. My old gym teacher used to let us rotate from station to station, but he never checked to see if we'd been to all of them.

The few times I had tried to climb the rope, I barely got off the ground. It's not like I have a huge hulk of a body to pull up. In fact, I'm actually kind of skinny. But my arm muscles would refuse to cooperate and I would just hang there. My body was like a lead sinker on a fishing line.

I avoided the rope as much as possible and spent more time on the tumbling mat and the balance beam. I have good balance from years of walking the porch rail at my old house.

Now, not only would I have to try to climb the rope, I would have to do it in front of a class full of strangers. Mr. Reynolds went on to talk about gym rules, but I wasn't paying much attention. I just kept staring up at the twist of rope that seemed to reach into outer space.

After Mr. Reynolds's announcements,

we counted off by fours. I was a four. Rope-climbing started with the threes. Luckily, we only had enough time left for one station that day. That meant I probably wouldn't get to that station until my next gym class. Maybe I could be sick that day.

After gym, I went to my locker to get my lunch. As I was dialing my combination, I heard someone say, "You're not too crazy about rope-climbing, are you?"

I turned to see a dark-skinned boy looking at me through thick glasses.

"Actually, I hate rope-climbing," I admitted. "How did you guess?"

"You looked like you were going to pass out when Mr. Reynolds was talking about it," explained the boy. He was wearing black jeans and a bright yellow T-shirt with a picture of a lizard coming out of its pocket.

"Every time I looked at you after that, you were just staring up at that rope like you were in a trance."

I laughed and said, "We never had to

climb ropes at my old school. I tried a few times, but I wasn't very good at it."

We started to walk toward the cafeteria.

"I'm James," said the boy.

"I'm Richard."

"You live in the old Miller place on Pine Street, don't you?" asked James.

"How did you know?"

"I've seen you in the backyard. I live on the street behind you, one house away. When I'm up in my tree house, I can see right into your yard."

I wasn't too crazy about the idea of someone spying on me, but I let it pass. "That's your tree house?" I asked. I had seen the back of it from my yard. It sat high in the branches of a big oak tree.

"Yeah. My dad and I built it a few years ago. Do you want to come over after school today and see it?"

"Sure," I said. "Thanks."

By this time, we had reached the cafeteria. I paused at the door and looked around. Students could sit anywhere, but most had already staked out their regular tables. For the first few days, I had moved around, sitting on the fringes of groups that were caught up in their own conversations.

James must have noticed that I was hesitating because he said, "Want to come and eat at my table?" He pointed to a table where two boys were already sitting.

"Okay," I said, relieved. James introduced me to his friends Michael and Roland. At lunch, we compared schedules. It turned out that James was in two of my afternoon classes. He told me all about the good teachers and the bad ones, and about the subjects that he liked least and most. Roland teased him about being a "brain," but James just laughed.

"If I'm a brain, then you're a spleen," he told Roland.

After school, I grabbed a handful of chocolate chip cookies and cut across the backyard to James's tree house.

"Hi," called a voice from somewhere

above me. James poked his head out of the doorway and looked down. "Come on up."

I studied the tree. As far as I could tell, the only way to get up to the tree house was by climbing a rope that was tied to a nearby branch.

"Thanks a lot," I said. "I suppose this is your idea of a joke?" I turned to walk back home.

"Wait a minute!" James shouted. "I just wanted to help you. I figured maybe I could teach you to climb it."

He sounded pretty sincere. I went back to the base of the tree. "Do you think you could?" I asked.

"We can try," said James. He caught hold of the rope and slid to the ground. "Let's see what you can do."

I wiped my hands on my pants. Then I reached up and grabbed the rope. I bent my knees and lifted my feet from the ground. As much as I strained, I could not pull myself up any farther. I just hung there while James studied me.

"I see your first mistake right

away," he announced. I stood up and let go of the rope.

"First of all, you're expecting your arms to do all of the work," said James. "Didn't you ever watch anyone climb a rope? Their legs do a lot of the work. Watch."

He took hold of the rope with his hands and wrapped his legs around the bottom of it. The rope was clenched between his sneakers. James reached higher with his hands and pulled himself up. At the same time, his feet pushed downward. He repeated this movement over and over, like an inchworm, until he had reached the top of the rope. Then, hand over hand, he lowered himself to the ground.

"Your arms can rest a little while your feet are gripping the rope," explained James. "Try it. And don't put your hands so high this time."

I took the rope in my hands and wrapped my legs around it. I tried to clasp the bottom with my sneakers. The rope kept slipping through my feet. I let go.

"You can't use the bottom of your feet to grab the rope," said James. "You've got to use the sides."

This time, while I held the rope with my hands, James tried to position my feet.

"Okay," he said. "Try straightening your legs."

I pushed down, and managed to raise myself several inches.

"Good," said James. "Now hold on with your feet and move your hands up."

I was able to move them up an inch or so. I repeated the motion, inching my way up the rope. After I had climbed a foot or so, I stopped to rest.

"Try not to stop," James advised. "It will only tire out your arms more."

James was right. I shouldn't have stopped. When I tried to climb higher, my arms refused to cooperate. I jumped down, falling to my knees.

I tried again and again. After a

while, I was able to climb halfway up the rope before I stopped.

"Keep going!" yelled James.

"I can't. My arms are getting shaky. I need to rest for a while." I let go of the rope and jumped down.

"You always get to the same spot and freeze," James commented. "The rope in the gym is twice as high as this one. You'll never make it to the top at this rate."

"Thanks a lot, coach."

James grinned. "No problem. We can try again tomorrow."

After that, we went back to my house for a while. I showed James my room. He looked at my books and was excited to find HATCHET by Gary Paulsen. He said that he had been wanting to read it. I let him borrow it. He was especially interested in my baseball card collection. It turned out that he collects, too. He admired my poster of Ryne Sandberg.

"He's my favorite player," I

explained. "He was born on my birth-day."

"Don't you mean you were born on HIS birthday?" James asked.

When he left to go home for dinner, he said, "See you tomorrow at the top of the rope."

♠

The next day, I headed over to the tree house as soon as my chores were done. I usually go to my dad's house for the weekend, but he was away on a busi-ness trip.

James was already in the tree house. "Ready to do it?" he called.

I shoved the sleeves of my shirt up and grabbed the rope.

"Now remember," James said, "Just keep going, no matter what."

I started to climb. The night's sleep must have done me good. My arms felt strong again. I still wasn't setting any speed record for climbing, but I passed my old stopping point with no problem.

Little by little I worked my way

up the rope until my eyes were at tree-house level. I stared. A card was propped against the door frame of the tree house. I looked closer. It was a Ryne Sandberg rookie card.

"Keep going and it's yours," James promised.

"Now you tell me," I grunted. "I shouldn't have stopped to look at it."

My arms were getting shaky, and my feet slipped. I was much too high to drop to the ground.

"C'mon. Just a few more feet," James coaxed.

I took a deep breath and strained to pull myself up. Slowly, I climbed high enough to put my foot inside the doorway. I swung myself over and landed on the floor.

"Congratulations!" proclaimed James. He handed me the baseball card.

"Thanks." I grinned. I couldn't believe that I'd done it.

There's only one thing I forgot to tell you," said James.

"What?" I asked.

"Climbing down is a lot harder than climbing up."

I groaned.

We stayed up in the tree house for a long time that morning, looking at James's stuff. He had been reading HATCHET up there and was already halfway through it. He kept a metal fishing tackle box in the tree house all of the time. In it were an old battery-operated radio, gum, hard candy, a flashlight, a small notebook, and a pencil.

We talked a lot, too. I told James about my old house and yard, and about my mom and dad getting a divorce.

He told me about his best friend who had moved away at the beginning of summer. I was secretly glad that his friend had moved. If he hadn't, James wouldn't have been in the market for a new best friend.

Climbing down wasn't as bad as James had made it out to be. I just worked my way down slowly. James told me that he and his family were going away the next day, but that I should practice as much as I wanted.

On Sunday, I climbed the rope a dozen times or so. On my last climb of the day, I left a message for James in his tackle box notebook.

It said, "See you in gym class from the top of the rope!"

●

Next gym class, it was my group's turn at the rope-climbing station. I was fourth in line. The first two boys climbed up with no problem. The third boy didn't even make it off the ground. Mr. Reynolds told him to watch how everyone else did it, then to try again later.

It was my turn. I grabbed the rope and slowly started to climb. My hands were tender from practicing all weekend. My gym shorts were more slippery than the jeans that I had been wearing.

About halfway up, I almost stopped to rest. My hands were throbbing and my arms were starting to get that old shaky feeling. I didn't think I could go on.

Just then, I spotted James watching me from the sit-up station. He grinned and gave me a thumbs-up sign. I kept going.

Before I knew it, I had reached the top. I looked around for a few seconds. I was even higher than the basketball hoops. I had never paid much attention to the outline of the basketball court which was painted on the floor. From up above, its colorful boundaries stood out clearly.

Slowly I made my way back down. I knew that if I stopped to rest, my arms would give out. When I reached the bottom, Mr. Reynolds said, "Good job, Richard."

I didn't even know that he knew my name. He made a check mark on a list.

I looked up at the top of the rope. Thanks to James, I had seen the world from a place I'd never been before. I guess that's one of the things that friends do best.

Proverb Three

WHEN IN ROME, DO AS THE ROMANS DO
or My Secret Weekend Life

Most people probably think that divorces happen when couples argue a lot. My parents really didn't argue much. In fact, they really didn't talk much. I remember going to my friends' houses and thinking about how noisy those places were. Things were usually pretty quiet around my house.

I'm not really sure how my parents ever got together in the first place. They don't have much in common.

Dad is a landscape architect. He met Mom when he was designing the land-scaping for the office building where she worked as an accountant. While they were dating, they used to go for long walks in some of the older neighborhoods around the city. That's when they first saw our old house and knew they had to have it. After they were married, they spent a few years restoring the house and landscaping it.

Then they had me. Mom was always happy to stay home. She loves to putter around and work in the garden. She has a few close friends that she sees a lot. Dad is much more outgoing and athletic. He loves to bike and hike, and to meet new people. Mom worries about everything and Dad doesn't worry about anything.

They don't look like they go together either. Dad is tall and has dark brown hair. He told me once that his nickname in college was "Beak" because of his big nose. His job takes him outdoors a lot, so his arms are very tan. Mom is short and fair-skinned. She burns if she stays out in the sun for very long. Her hair is the same color as mine.

In fact, she and I have almost the same shaggy haircut.

After a while, they started going their separate ways more and more. I did lots of things with each of them, but we never did much all together.

One night I was up in my bedroom working on math homework. Mom and Dad came in and sat down on the edge of my bed. I could tell right away that something was wrong.

Dad told me that they had decided to get a divorce. Looking back, I shouldn't have been as surprised as I was. I was pretty upset, too. I kept asking them to name one good reason for the divorce.

They kept telling me that it wasn't that simple. In fact it was very complicated, they said. Come to think of it, they never did give me that one good reason.

What bothers me most about the divorce is that I can't really say how I feel about Dad to my mom. Whenever I get ready to go to his apartment for the weekend, Mom starts to act funny. She'll say things like, "I hope your father doesn't fill you full of junk food." Or, "I don't know how you can get a good night's sleep on that horrible fold-out sofa your father has."

It almost seems like she wants me to be mad at Dad, too. Maybe she's afraid that I'll end up liking him more than her. So when I'm at home with Mom, we just go about our everyday lives, pretending that Dad doesn't exist.

I always have a great time with Dad. He still makes me do my homework and help with the housework, but he's a lot more relaxed about things than Mom. He may not cook gourmet meals for me. In fact, we usually order take-out food or cook hamburgers. And he doesn't always see if I've brushed my teeth or if I'm wearing my hat and gloves in the winter. But he never talks meanly about Mom the way she does about him.

I wish I could tell Mom how much it

upsets me when she does that. Even if Dad isn't her husband anymore, he's still my father.

When I get home from visiting Dad, I can always expect to be grilled by Mom. Here's a typical Sunday night conversation between us.

MOM: Did you have fun at your father's?

ME: Yeah.

MOM: What did you do?

ME: We rented a movie Friday night and got a pizza. Yesterday we hiked Crawford Creek.

MOM: Crawford Creek? Isn't that dangerous?

ME: Not really.

MOM: Did you eat anything besides pizza all weekend?

ME: We cooked out on the grill last night.

MOM: Was anyone else there?

ME: A couple of friends from Dad's work.

What I would really like to tell Mom
is that I had a GREAT time with Dad.
Crawford Creek was amazing. It probably
was a little bit dangerous. We climbed
down these really steep banks to get
there. I slipped on a rock and almost
fell into the creek. The friends that
came for dinner included a woman named
Lynn. She works for Dad's company. She
seems very nice. We talked about baseball for a long time. I think Dad is
interested in her. I think they've
already even dated.

But I never say any of those things
to Mom. I feel like a traitor to Dad, but
I can't bring myself to tell Mom how
I really feel. If I even begin to talk
about Dad, she looks angry. I know it
upsets her, so I just keep my mouth shut
and continue to lead my secret life
with Dad.

Proverb Four

IF AT FIRST YOU DON'T SUCCEED,
TRY, TRY AGAIN
or How My Writing Has Improved

One night, I was looking through the things that I kept in my book bank. I came across three or four stories that I had written when I was little. Ever since first grade, I have liked writing stories, comics, and plays.

I used to stage puppet shows for Mom and Dad on our old porch. I would make a whole cast of paper-bag puppets out of brown lunch bags. You just draw or glue on a face, stick your hand in the bag, and use the flap for the mouth. The only problem was that the puppets always looked like they were smiling big, broad smiles. It was hard to perform a dramatic fight or death scene when a puppet had that silly grin on its face.

I like writing for fun, but as soon as you tack the word "assignment" onto something, it becomes torture. The same thing goes for reading.

I love a good book. But give me the same book and tell me that I have to read it for school, and it suddenly becomes an ordeal. I start counting the number of pages that I have left and setting deadlines for myself. Then the pressure is really on. I'll put off the reading until I practically have to read the whole book in one night. Don't ask me why. I guess it's human nature.

Anyway, this is one of the stories that I wrote when I was in second grade.

THE RED WAGIN

Once upon a time there was a little red wagin. All the other wagins playd hide an seek but this wagin had a rusty weel and when it tryed to hide the other wagins found it right a way because it couldn't hide because it squeeked. Then the wagin would cry. Then the other wagins laughed and said don't cry because you will be more rusty and squeek more.

They left the red wagin there on the side walk. Then a little boy came a long and said don't cry because my dad can fix you. Then he took the red wagin home and his dad put oil on it. Then they lived happily ever after. The end.

●

Now can you see how much I've improved, Mr. Best?

Proverb Five

ABSENCE MAKES THE HEART GROW FONDER
or The First Time I Saw a Dead Body

Mom and I were sitting at the kitchen table one night when the phone rang. One of our old neighbors was calling to tell us that Harry Marshall had died.

All I could picture was Harry waving goodbye after I'd retrieved my key from the old house. I remembered how shrunken he had looked that day, and I felt sad.

"Apparently he had a heart attack last night," Mom told me. "By the time the ambulance got there, he was gone."

I always wonder why adults don't like to use the word "died." They usually say "passed away," or "gone." Maybe they have a hard time facing up to death, since it's creeping closer all the time.

Mom decided to make a pan of lasagna to take over to the Marshalls, since their kids would be coming back home for the funeral. She also told me that there would be visiting hours at the funeral home the next night.

"You're old enough to go, if you want to," said Mom. "I think it would be nice if you went, for Vi's sake."

Whenever Mom gives me her opinion about something, I might as well go along with it. It will save a lot of grief later on.

❧

The next night, we left the house a little before seven. I was dressed in my good black pants and a royal blue knit shirt. I thought Mom would make me wear my suit, but she said that these kinds of things were much more casual than they used to be.

My stomach was a little queasy as we walked into the funeral home. I had never seen a dead body, or a dead body's family before. What if I fainted or threw up or something? What would I say to Vi if she was crying?

Mom had told me that I didn't have to look at the body if I didn't feel like it. She just wanted me to say hi to Vi, and to tell Vi that I was sorry about Harry.

We walked into the lobby. There was a sign hanging by a doorway. It said "Harry J. Marshall." Below it, a guest book rested on a wooden table. Mom glanced through the pages before signing the book.

"Your father was here this afternoon," she remarked in that sarcastic tone of voice that she reserved only for him.

I signed the book below Mom's name. The sick feeling that I had in my stomach grew more intense. Suddenly, I did not want to do this.

I followed Mom into "Parlor A." It reminded me of somebody's living room. There were couches and easy chairs grouped next to the walls. Table lamps gave off a rosy glow.

At the far end of the room I could see the wooden casket. Huge sprays of flowers flanked both ends.

Groups of people were scattered here and there. I had expected everyone to be sitting around crying or praying, but they weren't doing that. They were talking in normal voices. I even heard one group laugh quietly at something. I relaxed a little.

I saw Vi standing with a couple near the casket. She waved when she saw us. Mom went over to Vi and hugged her. Then Vi turned and hugged me tightly.

"I'm so sorry about Harry," Mom said.

"Me too," I managed to add.

Tears glistened in Vi's eyes, but they didn't spill over. She turned toward the casket.

I glanced at Harry. He was dressed in a gray suit. His hands were clasped together just below his waist. Vi was telling Mom about Harry's heart condition. Now that I had gotten up the courage to look at Harry, I couldn't resist staring at him.

Harry's pure white hair had always had a shocked look about it. Now it was slicked back with some kind of hair gel. His skin looked waxy and pale compared to the healthy pink of everything else in the room.

A small gold pin held Harry's tie in place. It gleamed against the grayness of everything around it, and so did the wedding band on his left hand. I wondered if the pin and the ring would be buried, too.

I looked at all of the flowers. Banners across them said "Loving Husband," "Dear Father," and "Brother."

I didn't even know that Harry had any brothers or sisters. It was hard to imagine him playing with them as a kid.

Just then, Vi touched my cheek. "We've missed you in the neighborhood, Richard," she said. "The other day, Harry was wondering how you like your new school. I think he really missed having you around." I was surprised to think that Harry could have felt that way.

She continued, "When you were little, Harry used to just love to sit out back and watch you on your swing set. 'Just like a little monkey,' he used to say."

We laughed. Some other people came up to speak to Vi. She thanked us for coming and for the lasagna, and made us promise to visit her soon.

Mom and I stepped closer to the casket and looked at Harry one more time. I guess I was supposed to be saying a prayer, but instead I just thought about the last time I'd seen Harry.

Mom turned to leave, but I stayed for a few seconds.

"Thanks again, Harry," I whispered, and then I left. I could have sworn that I detected the faint odor of licorice in the air.

$$\begin{array}{r} 2.98 \\ +.24 \\ \hline \$3.22 \end{array}$$

Proverb Six

A PENNY SAVED IS A PENNY EARNED
or How I Bought My
Deluxe Colored Pencil Set

On the way home from my old grade
school, there was a corner drugstore
called Thompson's. Mr. Thompson was the
pharmacist, and his wife worked at the
checkout counter. The store carried
a little bit of everything: medicine,
magazines, cosmetics, school supplies,

toys, greeting cards, and more. It also had the best candy counter of any store around.

Lots of kids would stop there after school to stock up on candy and gum. My personal favorites were red string licorice and chocolate covered raisins. Around Halloween, I was also very partial to candy corn (the original white, yellow, and orange kind, not the mutant chocolate ones). My parents used to joke that Mr. Thompson had been paid off by the local dentists to rot out all of the children's teeth.

A few years ago, I was in Thompson's with my mom. I was wandering through the aisles as I had done hundreds of times before when I noticed a new item in the school supply section.

It was a deluxe set of twenty-four colored pencils. They came in a flat tin box that was painted with a picture of the pencils. There were three sets. I opened one of them.

The pencils were sharpened to perfect

points. The rich colors offered endless possibilities compared to my set of eight basic colors at home. I was going through a comic-book-writing phase at that time. I knew that I had to have them.

I looked at the bottom of the tin. The price was $2.98. This presented a slight problem. You see, Mom had bought Harry and Vi Marshall a potted plant to apologize for my bike tracks in their new driveway. She and Dad were withholding my allowance until the plant was paid for. I knew that there was no point in asking them for the money.

When we got home, I took the plug out of the bottom of my piggy bank and counted the change. I had $1.86. That meant I still needed $1.12 plus tax.

The solution was tossed my way the following Monday when I stopped at Thompson's after school to look at the pencils. I had asked Mrs. Thompson how much they would cost with tax.

"They'd come to $3.22," she reported.

"Shall I ring them up for you?"

"Maybe another day," I answered.

I walked out of the store and sat down on the bench that was right outside the door. As I was sitting there feeling sorry for myself, two junior-high boys came out of the store with bags of candy. I saw one of them toss a few pennies onto the sidewalk. The boys kept walking.

I waited until they had rounded the corner, then I went to pick up the pennies. There were three of them. I put them in my pocket. Lots of times, I had seen kids throw away pennies that they had received as change. In fact, it used to drive Mom crazy when she saw it happen.

"No one can afford to throw away a penny," she would say. "Or if they can afford it, they should donate their pennies to charity."

I began to look around the sidewalk. Under the bench, there were two more pennies. I added them to the collection in my pocket. My career as a penny-pincher had begun.

As I walked home that day, I remembered a riddle that my dad had told me. It went like this. Which would you rather have: a sports car or a penny doubled every day for a month?

Most people say the sports car, because they don't think the pennies will add up to much. It turns out that the penny is a much better choice, though. You'd start with one cent. The next day you'd have two cents, the third day four cents, and the fourth day eight cents. By the end of a week, you'd have sixty-four cents. By the end of the second week, you'd have $81.92. Now, get ready. By week three, you'd have $10,485.76. By the end of week four, you'd have a grand total of $1,342,177.28. (If you don't believe me, get a calculator and try it.)

Every day after school, I checked the outside of Thompson's. On the average, I found two or three pennies a day.

At that rate, I figured it would only take me a couple of weeks to have enough money to buy the pencils.

I started to look for coins in other places, too. I never passed a phone booth without stopping to check the coin return. I never actually found any coins there, but I did find a dime on the floor of a phone booth. Sometimes there would be a stray penny on a sidewalk, or in a store or parking lot. I really hit the jackpot when I found thirty-seven cents in the pocket of my old jeans.

Once, I was crossing a street near my house, and I saw a quarter lying in the middle of the intersection. Looking carefully to make sure no cars were coming, I bent down to pick it up. It was baked right into the tar. A car was approaching the stop sign. I decided that risking my life over twenty-five cents was not a good idea, so I hurried to the other corner. Every day, I had to pass that quarter on my way to school.

Finally, on an especially hot day

when the tar was soft, I was able to quickly pry it loose with a stone that was lying near the curb.

●

By the end of three weeks, I finally had enough money to buy the pencils. I put all of my coins into a paper bag and headed over to Thompson's. I hurried to the school supply section.

The pencils were gone.

Then I heard Mrs. Thompson ask, "Are these what you're looking for?"

I looked toward the counter. She held up a set of the pencils. "When the second set was sold, I put these away for you," she explained. "I know you've had your eye on them."

"Thanks! I finally have enough money," I told her.

I dumped the coins out onto the counter. Several pennies were stuck to the quarter that had been in the tar. Mrs. Thompson counted out all of my money.

"Just right," she announced.

She put the pencils in a bag for me. Then she reached over and put a box of chocolate covered raisins in the bag, too.

"These are for being such a loyal customer," said Mrs. Thompson.

I thanked her again and went home to try out my new colors.

By the way, I still pick up a penny whenever I see one.

Proverb Seven

TOO MANY COOKS SPOIL THE BROTH
or How Mom and I
Created Volcanic Salsa

It occurs to me that up until now, I've given my mom a bad rap. Other than not being able to talk normally about Dad, we really have a lot of fun together. Around other people, Mom is very quiet and shy. With me, she's a lot different.

We both love movies, popcorn, baseball, and roller coasters. Every summer, we've driven to a different amusement

park to try out the coasters. Mom likes
the older wooden ones best. She likes the
sound they make and says that they give
you a purer sense of being on a roller
coaster. My favorites are the loop-the-
loops. I love the feeling of being
upside-down.

We also like to cook things together.
We experiment with all kinds of concoc-
tions. Some of our more memorable ones
are Hawaiian Pizza (with ham and crushed
pineapple) and Chocolate Marshmallow
Banana Cream Pie. Even James, the
world's pickiest eater, liked that pie.

For a while, we were on a Mexican food
kick. We got really good at making tacos,
burritos, and enchiladas. We both like
them very spicy. We even decided to can
our own salsa sauce using tomatoes,
peppers, and onions that we grew in the
garden.

We cooked the salsa in a big electric
roaster oven. It filled the whole house
with a spicy, mouth-watering smell. What
Mom didn't know was that every time I

walked past the roaster, I added a few generous squirts of Tabasco sauce. What I didn't know was that Mom was doing the same thing.

Finally the sauce was ready to can. We filled and sealed a dozen jars and kept an unsealed one to use that week.

As we were cleaning up, Mom's boss, Nancy, stopped by to pick up some papers. Nancy commented on the wonderful aroma, so Mom gave her a jar of the salsa.

That night, we made tacos for dinner. Both Mom and I piled on gobs of our fresh sauce and dove in.

I have never tasted anything so spicy in my whole life. And you should have seen the look on Mom's face. We were practically breathing fire. That was when we realized what we had done. Later, when our taste buds had recovered, we laughed about the Tabasco.

Suddenly, a horrified expression came over Mom's face.

"Nancy!" she shrieked. "I hope she hasn't fed it to her family!"

Mom called Nancy to explain. She hung up the phone a few minutes later.

"That was Nancy's husband," she said, laughing. "It seems that Nancy took the kids for ice cream. They ate something very hot for dinner and they're still trying to cool down their throats. He just got home from work as they were walking out the door. I didn't bother to explain to him what happened. I just hope that I have a job tomorrow."

Mom did have her job the next day. Nancy laughed as much as we did about the whole thing. And we changed the canning labels to read "Volcanic Salsa." Whenever we open a new jar of it, we mix it with some very mild salsa. It comes out just right.

We laugh every time, though. I guess in some recipes, humor is a basic ingredient.

Proverb Eight

HASTE MAKES WASTE

or How I Slipped in Crawford Creek

Autumn is my favorite time of the year. I love crunching through the leaves as I walk to school and tossing a football around with James before dinner. The only drawbacks about fall that I can see are that school has begun and baseball has ended.

Last weekend, I stayed at Dad's place. On Saturday, it was raining. We went to the mall for a movie. We happened to walk past a sporting goods store where there was a display of hiking boots in the window.

"If we're going to do any serious hiking, you should really have a pair of good boots," Dad said. "Those sneakers you wear could actually be dangerous. They don't give you proper support or traction."

I tried on several pairs. Dad bought the ones that I liked best. They were forest green with purple nylon laces. They were also waterproof.

On the way home, Dad suggested that we do an all-day hike at Crawford Creek the next day. "The leaves are at peak color, and it's supposed to be sunny tomorrow," he pointed out. Then he paused.

"How would you feel if I invited my friend Lynn to come along?"

"It's okay with me," I answered.

It really was okay with me. Lynn had seemed nice the few times that I'd met her. But I was already wondering what to

tell Mom if she asked me too many ques-
tions about my weekend with Dad.

♠

The next morning, we got up early and
packed three lunches. Dad loaded them
into his backpack, along with bug spray
and his small first-aid kit.

Lynn was waiting on her porch when we
pulled into her driveway. She was
dressed in the same uniform that we were:
jeans, a T-shirt, and hiking boots. Her
short dark hair was almost completely
hidden by a baseball cap. She carried a
brick-shaped package wrapped in tin-
foil.

I got out of the car so that Lynn
could sit in the front.

"Hi, Richard," she said, smiling. "I
don't mind sitting in the back."

"Oh, that's okay," I said.

"Well, thanks," said Lynn.

We got into the car. Lynn gave Dad
a quick kiss. "I'm so glad you guys
invited me!" she said.

"What's in the package?" Dad asked.

"I thought we could use some fudge brownies," answered Lynn.

"Mmmm. Definitely a necessity for survival in the wilderness," Dad said.

During the ride to Crawford Creek, we talked about the World Series that had recently ended.

Then Lynn turned to me. "When your Dad called, he told me that you got new hiking boots," she remarked.

I stuck my foot up in the air so that Lynn could see them from the front seat of the car. She liked them a lot.

We parked the car and set off along the trail that leads to the creek. After about ten minutes, we could see the walls of the creek in front of us. We carefully climbed down the steep path.

Once we were at the bottom, we had to cross the creek right away. The good hiking was on the other shore, where part of the rocky creek bed was exposed.

To cross the creek, we had to step on a series of rocks that had been placed by hikers over the years. Some of the rocks stuck out of the water, and others were just below the surface.

Dad went first. He carefully tested each rock to see if it was stable.

"Watch out," he warned. "These under-water rocks are very slippery. Make sure you have good traction on them before you step off."

Lynn and I slowly made our way across. The last step was a long one. Dad had to jump to reach the shore. He waited there to reach a hand to Lynn and me to help us across from the last rock.

We hiked the creek bed for quite a way. In most places, the water was only a foot or so deep. Once in a while, we came to a place where rocks had formed a natural dam, making a deeper pool. Those places were great for skipping stones.

We had a contest to find out who could get the most skips. Lynn and I tied at seven skips each. The most Dad could get was four.

"It's all in the wrist," Lynn told him.

Around noon, we found a flat, shady spot on the bank to have our picnic lunch. Dad and I had brought peanut butter and jelly sandwiches, cheese and crackers, apples, and small cartons of orange juice.

"Why does a simple peanut butter sandwich taste so much better out here?" Dad wondered.

Lynn's brownies made an excellent ending to the meal. We packed up and headed back.

I arrived at the crossing point ahead of Dad and Lynn. I guess I was feeling carefree and overconfident because I went ahead and jumped right over to that first rock.

As soon as my foot hit it, I knew that I was in trouble. My boot skidded across the surface of the rock. I swung my arms wildly as I tried to catch my balance, but it was no use.

As I went down, I tried to grab the rock with my right hand. The edge of the rock was very sharp. When I stood up

in the knee-deep water, I saw blood
dripping from my palm. I waded the rest
of the way across the creek.

Just then, Dad and Lynn came around
the bend and saw me.

"What happened?" they called.

"I sort of fell in," I answered.

They were laughing as they stepped
across the creek.

"Those boots may be waterproof," Dad
teased, "but not from the inside out."

Then he saw my hand.

Dad examined the cut. He got out the
first-aid kit and wrapped a gauze
bandage around my palm. The blood soaked
right through. Dad looked worried.

"That's a pretty deep gash," he said.
"I think we had better stop at the
medical center on the way home and have
someone take a look at it." Lynn agreed.

We hiked back up the trail to the car.
I felt stupid for ruining such a good
day.

On the way to the medical center,
Lynn told me about the time that she had

fallen off her bike at the corner of a busy intersection. She had sprained her wrist, but had mostly been embarrassed by the whole thing, she said. I think she was trying to make me feel less stupid.

At the center, I was given a tetanus shot. After that, a doctor gave me three more shots to numb my palm. Then she stitched up the cut. I couldn't imagine that the stitches would have hurt more than all of those shots. The doctor also gave me some pain pills for later.

We took Lynn home and then headed for Dad's place to change clothes and collect my stuff.

●

On the ride back to Mom's house, Dad and I were pretty quiet. I think we were both worried about what she would say.

"I guess I should have called your mother from the medical center," Dad said. "It isn't very nice of me to spring this accident on her."

Usually, Dad just drops me off in the driveway and waves to Mom when she opens the front door. This time, though, he came to the door with me.

As soon as Mom opened the door, she saw the bandage. Mothers have an instinct for zeroing in on things like that.

"What happened?" she asked angrily.

"I fell in the creek," I said quickly. "It's only three stitches."

Mom turned to Dad accusingly. "Why did you take him to that creek again?" she demanded. "I knew something like this would happen one of these times."

"Lots of people hike that creek," Dad said.

"It was my own fault," I tried to explain. "I tried to jump across instead of feeling my way like Dad showed me."

But Mom wouldn't listen. She told me to take my things upstairs and to get ready for dinner. I kissed Dad goodbye.

He said, "See you next week, Rich. I'll call you tomorrow."

As I headed up the stairs, I heard Mom tell Dad that we had plans for the next weekend and that I wouldn't be able to spend it with him. I knew that we really didn't have plans. I had a sick feeling in my stomach.

Why did I have to try to jump across to that rock, anyway? Why had I been in such a hurry?

Proverb Nine

THE PEN IS MIGHTIER THAN THE SWORD
or How My Voice Was Heard

On the night of my creek accident, I was lying on the couch after dinner, watching TV. By then, Mom had calmed down a little bit and had fixed me a hot fudge sundae for dessert. She even let me eat it in the living room.

During dinner, she asked me if my homework was done.

"I just have a few more math problems to do," I answered.

Mom offered to help me write them out

since it would be hard for me to use my right hand for a few days. She was sure that the teachers would understand why the work was in her handwriting.

I didn't think too much of it when Mom disappeared upstairs for a while. Then she came downstairs and turned off the TV.

I sat up straight on the couch. Mom came and sat beside me. I could tell that she had been crying. Then I saw the reason. She was holding the "proverbs" assignment.

"I wasn't snooping," Mom said softly. "I was looking for your math homework when I saw these...and read them."

I felt totally ashamed.

"I'm sorry, Mom," I said. "I didn't mean to hurt you."

At that, Mom looked startled. "No, I'M sorry," she replied. She looked down at my paper and hesitated.

"I haven't exactly encouraged you to talk about your father," she said. "You should be able to have a good time